Science

Cootie Catchers

Written by
Sharon L. Apichella and Mary D. Sutton

Editor: Christie Weltz
Cover Illustrator: Gloria Jenkins
Designer/Production: Karen Nguyen
Art Director: Moonhee Pak
Project Director: Stacey Faulkner

Table of Contents

Introduction

Cootie Catchers Science is an interactive and motivating tool for daily review. Using a new twist on the popular origami fortune tellers, this hands-on resource provides a fun and unique approach to practicing and reviewing standards-based science concepts and academic language. *Cootie Catchers Science* features 20 reproducible cootie catchers that each reinforce specific science concepts. Each page includes a *Before You Flip* hint for students to apply while they use each cootie catcher and an *After You Flip* activity to extend their learning after they have finished. Once the cootie catcher is made, students read and answer the questions; then they lift the flaps to reveal the correct answers. A recording sheet is provided to help teachers keep track of assigned cootie catchers.

Aligned to National Science Education Standards (NSES), *Cootie Catchers Science* is an ideal resource for providing specific review for all students. Research shows that repetition is essential for the brain to learn and recall information. Furthermore, children tend to repeat activities they enjoy. *Cootie Catchers Science* offers a fun and quick way for students to repeat and retain essential information. This teacher-tested, student-approved resource can be used for classroom center activities, as enrichment assignments when regular class work is completed, or for homework. Perfect for individuals, partners, or small groups, *Cootie Catchers Science* makes practicing science concepts enjoyable. The following areas are addressed in this resource:

* Life science
* Earth and space science
* Physical science

Cootie catchers fit in pants pockets, backpacks, or lunch boxes for review on the go! Students can use them in a classroom center, at their desks, on the playground, or in a car or bus. Parents can slip cootie catchers into a pocket or purse and use them to review with their child at home, in line at the store, or while waiting for appointments. With these easy-to-make, fun-to-use, portable manipulatives, students will love reviewing science concepts and vocabulary the *Cootie Catchers Science* way!

Getting Started

How to Use

1. Select a skill you would like your students to practice, and make multiple copies of the corresponding page. Store the pages in a labeled hanging file in a science center.

2. Demonstrate how to fold the cootie catchers. Display the instructions for students' reference.

3. Remind students to read the *Before You Flip* section before using each cootie catcher.

4. Have the students complete the *After You Flip* activity as an extension or quick assessment after they have used each cootie catcher. Ask the students to return the top portion of the page to you. Use this, along with the recording sheet, to keep track of assigned cootie catchers.

5. Send the cootie catchers home for additional practice.

How to Make

1. Carefully cut along the outline of the square. Fold and unfold the square in half diagonally in both directions to make two creases that form an X.

2. Place the paper facedown, and then fold each of the four corners in so that their points touch the center.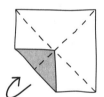

3. Turn the paper over so the flaps are facedown. Again, fold each of the four corners in so their points touch the center.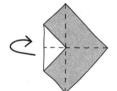

4. Fold the square in half, making a rectangle. Unfold and fold in half in the opposite direction, making a rectangle.

5. Slide both index fingers and thumbs under the four flaps.

6. Use your thumbs and index fingers to pinch the top corners together and form a point. You are ready to play.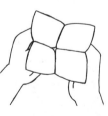

How to Play

1. Choose a number from one to five.

2. Open and close the cootie catcher (front to back and then sideways) as many times as the number selected.

3. Choose one of the four questions shown inside and answer it.

4. Lift the flap on which the question is written and check the answer.

5. Continue playing in the same way until all eight questions have been answered.

Animal Classification

Hint: Animals can be classified based on different observable characteristics.

On the back of this paper, name and classify the following animals:

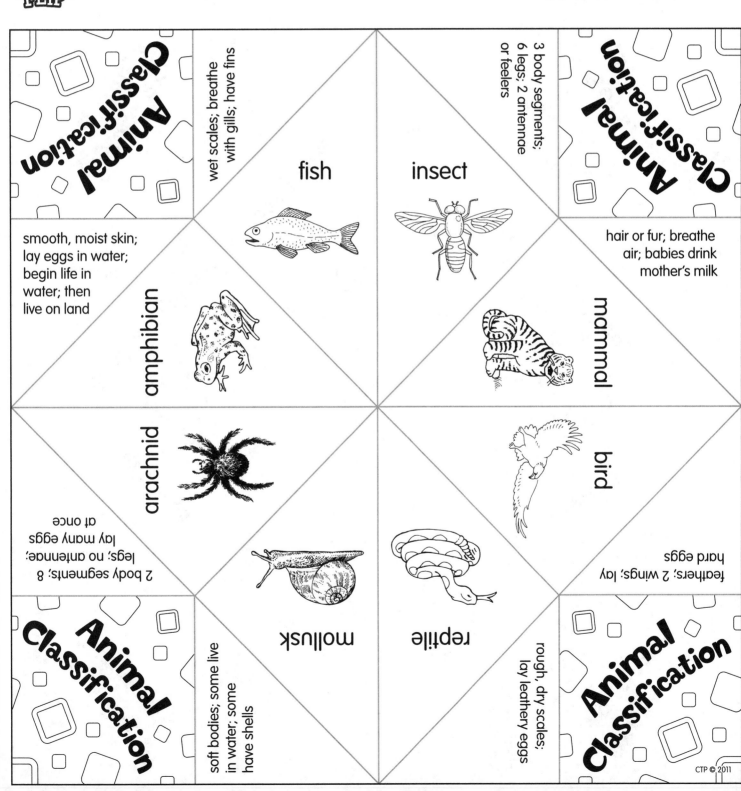

Animal Classification

wet scales; breathe with gills; have fins

fish

insect

3 body segments; 6 legs; 2 antennae or feelers

Animal Classification

smooth, moist skin; lay eggs in water; begin life in water; then live on land

amphibian

mammal

hair or fur; breathe air; babies drink mother's milk

arachnid

bird

2 body segments; 8 legs; no antennae; lay many eggs at once

mollusk

reptile

feathers; 2 wings; lay hard eggs

Animal Classification

soft bodies; some live in water; some have shells

rough, dry scales; lay leathery eggs

Animal Classification

Cootie Catchers • Science • Gr. 3 © 2011 Creative Teaching Press

CTP © 2011

Name _____   Date _____

Survival of Living Things

Before you "FLIP"

Hint: Plants and animals have special characteristics, or adaptations, that help them survive in their environment.

After you "FLIP"

On the back of this paper, explain how a bear's claws help it survive in its environment.

Survival of Living Things

These help an owl catch its prey.

This helps a chameleon blend into its surroundings.

Survival of Living Things

talons or claws

camouflage

Roses use these to protect themselves from hungry animals.

The skunk uses this to help it escape predators.

thorns

bad odor or smell

scent

ink cloud

Some flowers use color and *this* to attract pollinating insects.

This helps a squid distract predators so it can escape.

Survival of Living Things

rattle

spines

Survival of Living Things

The rattlesnake uses this to warn predators to stay away.

This helps a cactus keep insects and animals from damaging the plant.

Herbivore, Carnivore, or Omnivore?

Before you "FLIP"

Hint: Based on the foods they eat, animals belong to one of three groups: herbivores, carnivores, or omnivores.

After you "FLIP"

On the back of this paper, list two animals for each group: herbivores, carnivores, and omnivores.

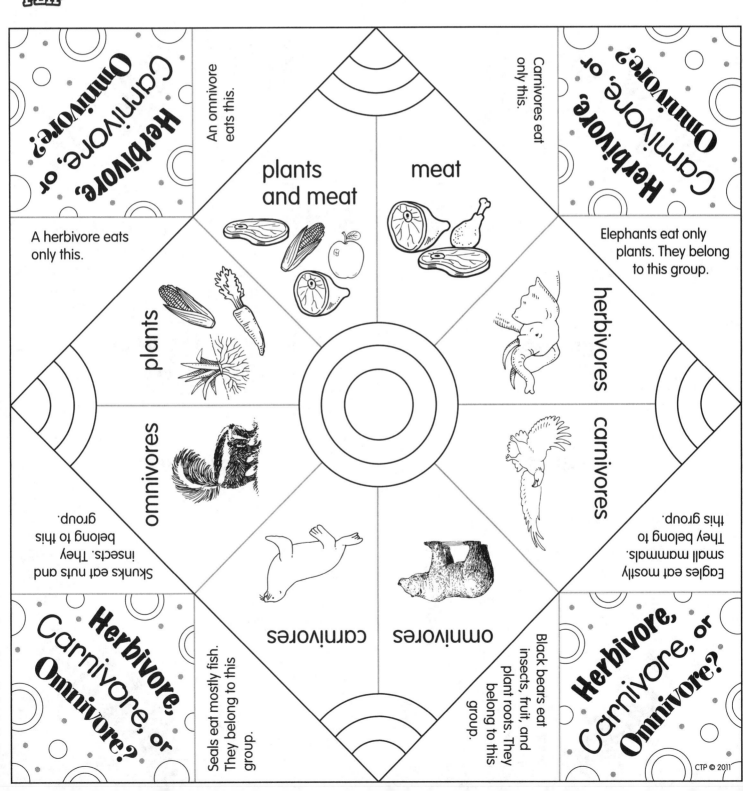

Herbivore, Carnivore, or Omnivore?

An omnivore eats this.

plants and meat

meat

Carnivores eat only this.

Herbivore, Carnivore, or Omnivore?

A herbivore eats only this.

plants

herbivores

Elephants eat only plants. They belong to this group.

omnivores

carnivores

carnivores

omnivores

Skunks eat nuts and insects. They belong to this group.

Eagles eat mostly small mammals. They belong to this group.

Herbivore, Carnivore, or Omnivore?

Seals eat mostly fish. They belong to this group.

Black bears eat insects, fruit, and plant roots. They belong to this group.

Herbivore, Carnivore, or Omnivore?

Name _____ Date _____

Food Chains

Hint: Food chains often include producers, consumers, decomposers, predators, and prey.

Label the decomposer, prey, and predator in the food chain to the right.

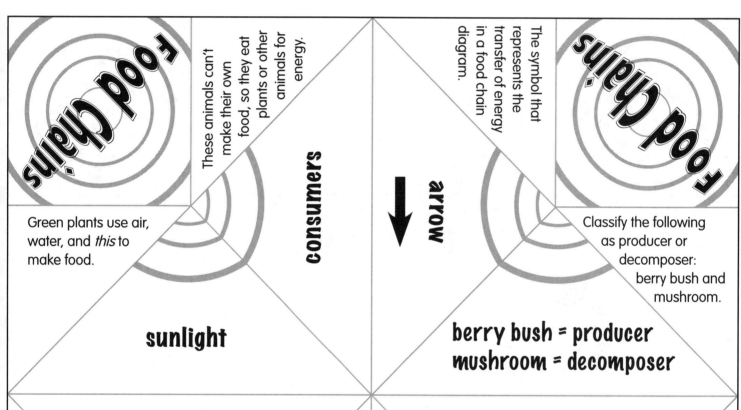

Green plants use air, water, and *this* to make food.

These animals can't make their own food, so they eat plants or other animals for energy.

consumers

The symbol that represents the transfer of energy in a food chain diagram.

arrow

Classify the following as producer or decomposer: berry bush and mushroom.

sunlight

berry bush = producer
mushroom = decomposer

predators

decomposers

prey

Animals that hunt other animals for food.

Organisms like green plants that make food for themselves.

producers

An animal that is hunted for food.

Organisms that help dead plants and animals decay.

Name _____   Date _____

Biomes

Before you "FLIP"

Hint: A biome is a large group of similar ecosystems. Examples include: Tundra, Forest (Deciduous Forest and Rain Forest), Desert, Grassland, Wetland, and Ocean.

After you "FLIP"

On the back of this paper, list at least one plant or animal that can be found in each of the biomes listed above.

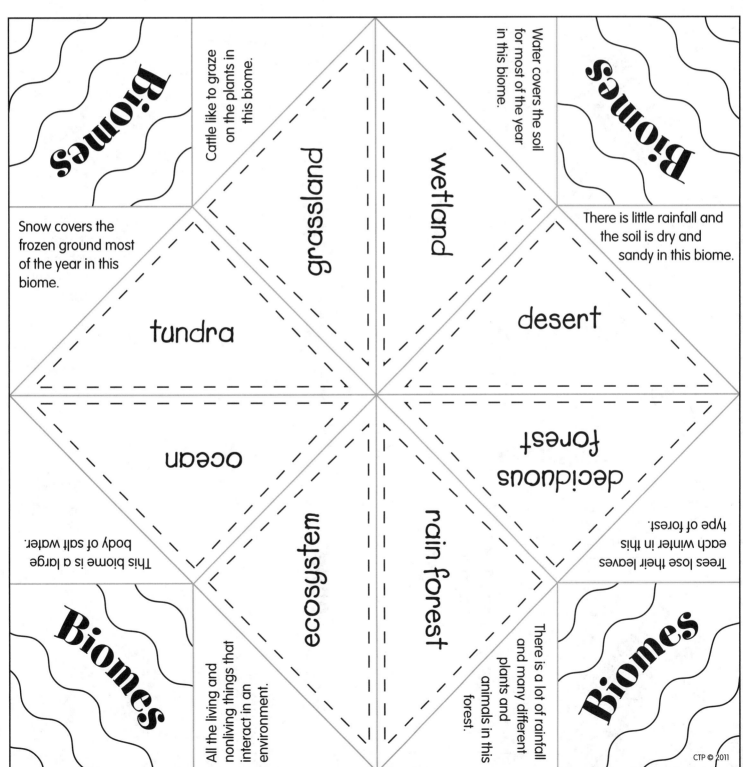

Biomes

Cattle like to graze on the plants in this biome.

Water covers the soil for most of the year in this biome.

Biomes

Snow covers the frozen ground most of the year in this biome.

grassland

wetland

There is little rainfall and the soil is dry and sandy in this biome.

tundra

desert

ocean

deciduous forest

This biome is a large body of salt water.

ecosystem

rain forest

Trees lose their leaves each winter in this type of forest.

Biomes

All the living and nonliving things that interact in an environment.

There is a lot of rainfall and many different plants and animals in this forest.

Biomes

Tropical Rain Forest

Before you "FLIP" **Hint:** Scientists divide the rain forest into four layers or zones.

After you "FLIP" On the back of this paper, list at least three animals or insects you would find in the canopy layer of the rain forest.

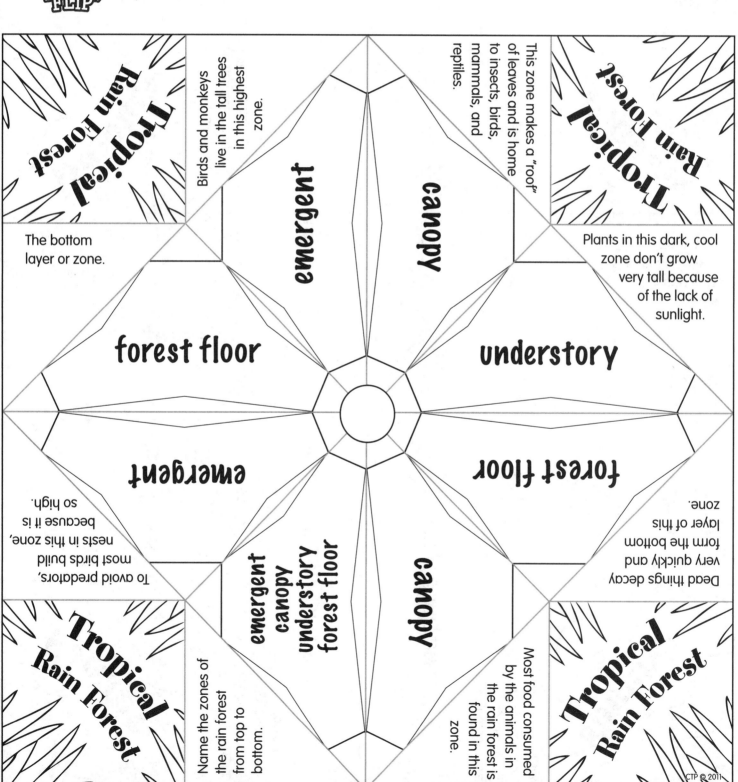

Tropical Rain Forest

Birds and monkeys live in the tall trees in this highest zone.

This zone makes a "roof" of leaves and is home to insects, birds, mammals, and reptiles.

Tropical Rain Forest

emergent

canopy

The bottom layer or zone.

Plants in this dark, cool zone don't grow very tall because of the lack of sunlight.

forest floor

understory

emergent

forest floor

To avoid predators, most birds build nests in this zone, because it is so high.

Dead things decay very quickly and form the bottom layer of this zone.

Tropical Rain Forest

emergent
canopy
understory
forest floor

canopy

Tropical Rain Forest

Name the zones of the rain forest from top to bottom.

Most food consumed by the animals in the rain forest is found in this zone.

Changing Environments

Before you "FLIP"   **Hint:** Plants and animals are affected by changes to their environment.

After you "FLIP"   On the back of this paper, explain how a drought might change an environment.

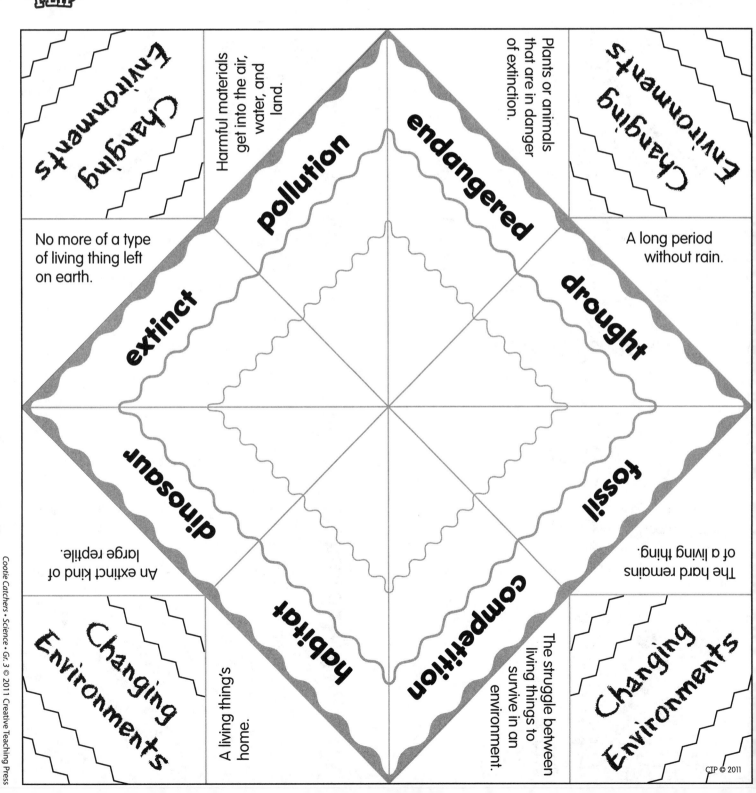

Changing Environments

Harmful materials get into the air, water, and land.

Plants or animals that are in danger of extinction.

Changing Environments

pollution

endangered

No more of a type of living thing left on earth.

A long period without rain.

extinct

drought

dinosaur

fossil

An extinct kind of large reptile.

The hard remains of a living thing.

Changing Environments

habitat

competition

Changing Environments

A living thing's home.

The struggle between living things to survive in an environment.

Name _____ Date _____

How Do Plants Survive?

Before you "FLIP"

Hint: Each plant part has a special job that helps the plant survive.

After you "FLIP"

On the back of this paper, predict what would happen to a plant if the leaves were removed.

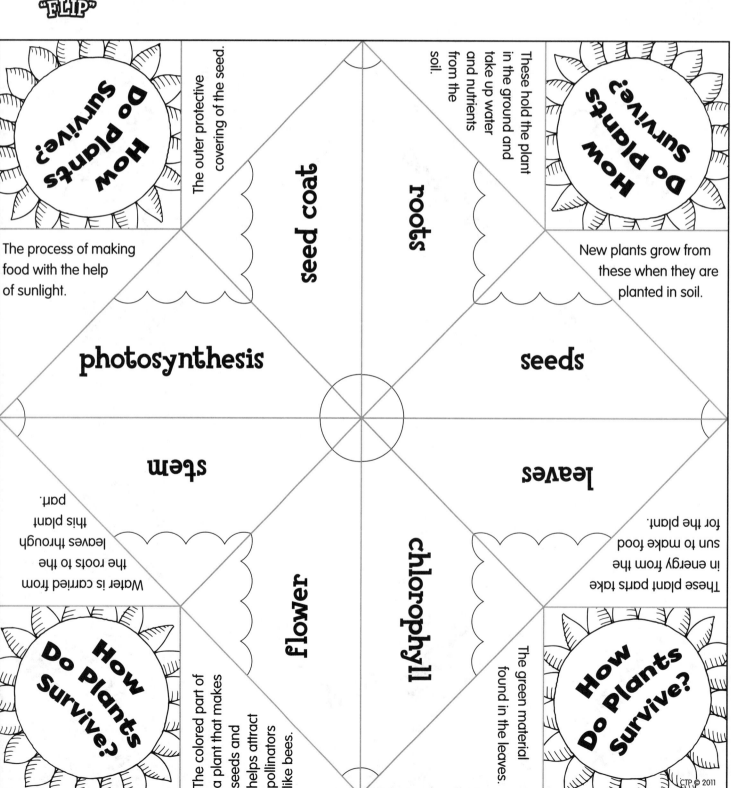

How Do Plants Survive?

The outer protective covering of the seed.

seed coat

roots

These hold the plant in the ground and take up water and nutrients from the soil.

How Do Plants Survive?

The process of making food with the help of sunlight.

photosynthesis

seeds

New plants grow from these when they are planted in soil.

stem

leaves

Water is carried from the roots to the leaves through this plant part.

These plant parts take in energy from the sun to make food for the plant.

How Do Plants Survive?

The colored part of a plant that makes seeds and helps attract pollinators like bees.

flower

chlorophyll

The green material found in the leaves.

How Do Plants Survive?

CTP © 2011

Plants Make Their Own Food

Before you "FLIP"   **Hint:** Photosynthesis happens when plants make food using air, water, nutrients, and sunlight.

After you "FLIP"   On the back of this paper, explain why the process of photosynthesis is helpful to organisms that breathe oxygen.

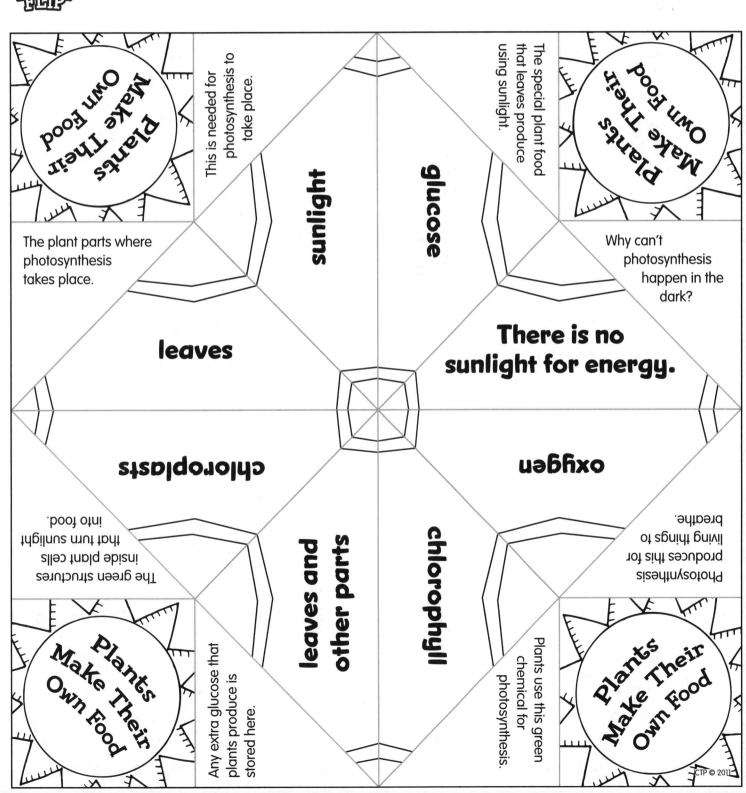

Plants Make Their Own Food

This is needed for photosynthesis to take place.

The special plant food that leaves produce using sunlight.

Plants Make Their Own Food

The plant parts where photosynthesis takes place.

sunlight

glucose

Why can't photosynthesis happen in the dark?

leaves

There is no sunlight for energy.

chloroplasts

oxygen

The green structures inside plant cells that turn sunlight into food.

leaves and other parts

chlorophyll

Photosynthesis produces this for living things to breathe.

Plants Make Their Own Food

Any extra glucose that plants produce is stored here.

Plants use this green chemical for photosynthesis.

Plants Make Their Own Food

CTP © 2011

14 Name _____   Date _____

Earth's Resources

Hint: Earth has two kinds of resources:
  Renewable resources are things that can be remade or replaced by nature.
  Nonrenewable resources are things that either cannot be remade or take thousands of years to regrow.

On the back of this paper, describe how you can conserve one of earth's resources.

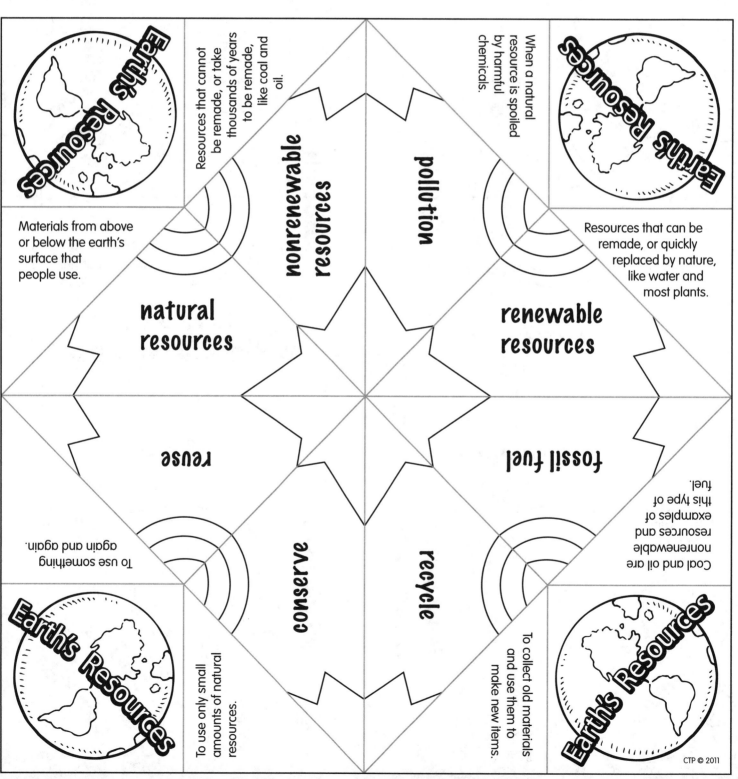

Cootie Catchers • Science • Gr. 3 © 2011 Creative Teaching Press

Name _____   Date _____

Seasons

Hint: Seasons occur because the earth turns on its tilted axis as it orbits the sun.

What season is it in the Southern Hemisphere when it is summer in the Northern Hemisphere?

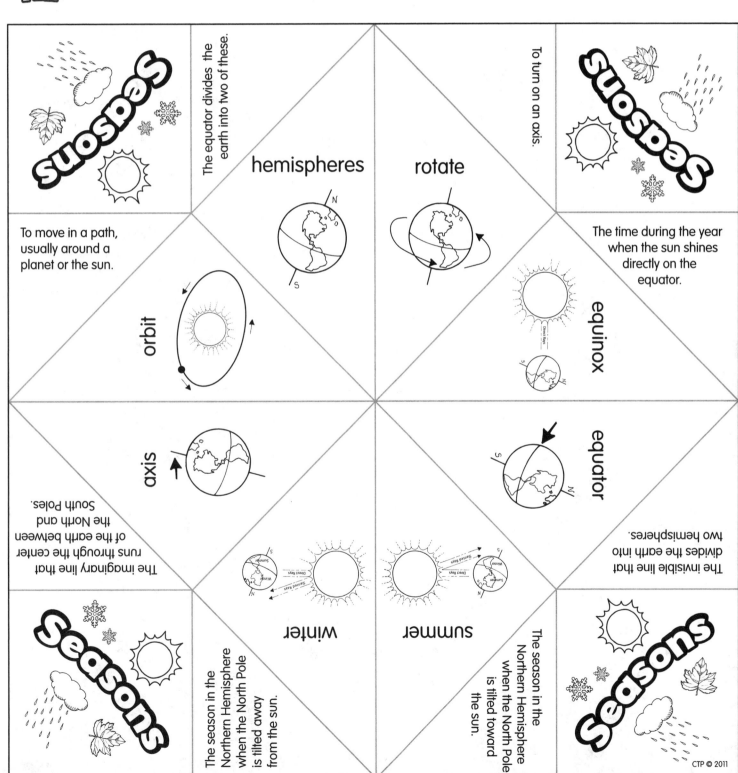

CTP © 2011

Name _____ Date _____

The Atmosphere

Before you "FLIP"

Hint: Earth is covered by a blanket of air that protects it from the sun's harmful rays, extreme temperatures, and space objects.

After you "FLIP"

On the back of this paper, list at least three types of precipitation.

The Atmosphere

Any form of water that falls from clouds to earth's surface.

The measure of how hot or cold something is.

The Atmosphere

The layers of air that cover the earth's surface.

precipitation

temperature

The movement of water between the air and the earth as it changes state.

atmosphere

water cycle

condensation

water vapor

The process of water as a gas changing into a liquid.

Water as an invisible gas.

The Atmosphere

evaporation

weather

The Atmosphere

The process of liquid water changing into a gas.

The condition of the atmosphere at a certain place and time.

CTP © 2011

Phases of the Moon

Before you "FLIP"

Hint: On average, it takes the moon a little more than 27 days to orbit the earth.

After you "FLIP"

Name the phases of the moon.

_____ _____ _____ _____ _____

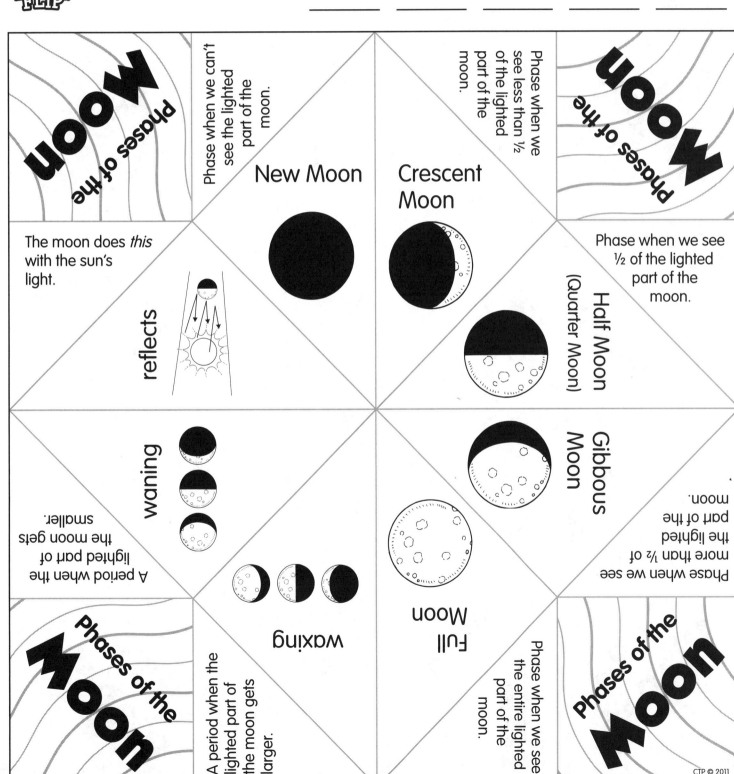

Phases of the MOON

Phase when we can't see the lighted part of the moon.

Phase when we see less than ½ of the lighted part of the moon.

Phases of the MOON

New Moon

Crescent Moon

The moon does *this* with the sun's light.

Phase when we see ½ of the lighted part of the moon.

reflects

Half Moon (Quarter Moon)

waning

Gibbous Moon

A period when the lighted part of the moon gets smaller.

Phase when we see more than ½ of the lighted part of the moon.

Phases of the MOON

waxing

Full Moon

Phase when we see the entire lighted part of the moon.

Phases of the MOON

A period when the lighted part of the moon gets larger.

Name _____   Date _____

The Planets

Before you "FLIP"

Hint: There are eight planets that orbit the sun.

After you "FLIP"

On the back of this paper, explain why Mercury would not be a safe place to live.

The Planets

The Planets

2nd planet from the sun; thick, cloudy atmosphere; rocky surface

3rd planet from the sun; one moon; surface of rock and water

Venus

Earth

1st planet from the sun; no moons; thin atmosphere

4th planet from the sun; two moons; rocky surface of red dust

Mercury

Mars

Neptune

Jupiter

8th planet from the sun; over 10 known moons; faint rings made of dust

5th planet from the sun; largest planet; storms in its atmosphere

The Planets

Uranus

Saturn

The Planets

7th planet from the sun; rotates on its side; gas giant

6th planet from the sun; over 50 known moons; large rings

CTP © 2011

The Solar System

Hint: The Solar System is made up of the sun and all objects that orbit around it.

On the back of this paper, describe at least five objects you might see if you looked at the solar system through a telescope.

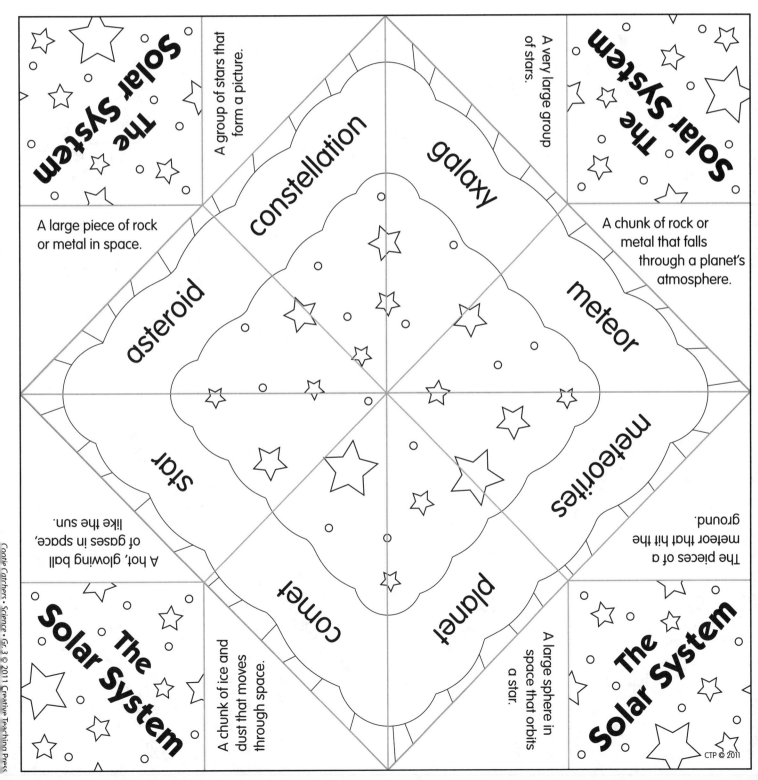

Name _____   Date _____

Building Blocks of Matter

Before you "FLIP"   **Hint:** Matter is anything that has mass and takes up space.

After you "FLIP"   On the back of this paper, explain the relationship between atoms, elements, and matter.

Building Blocks of Matter

A measure of the amount of matter in something.

mass

carbon

A basic element found in most living things.

Building Blocks of Matter

The smallest unit of an element.

atom

element

A basic building block of matter made of atoms.

nonmetals

A group of elements that are poor conductors of electricity or heat.

property

A trait of something that can be observed or measured.

Building Blocks of Matter

A group of elements that conduct heat and electricity.

metals

periodic table

A chart that lists the known elements and their properties.

Building Blocks of Matter

Cootie Catchers • Science • Gr 3 © 2011 Creative Teaching Press

Matter Changes

Hint: Matter can be changed physically and chemically.

On the back of this paper, give at least one example each of a physical change and a chemical change.

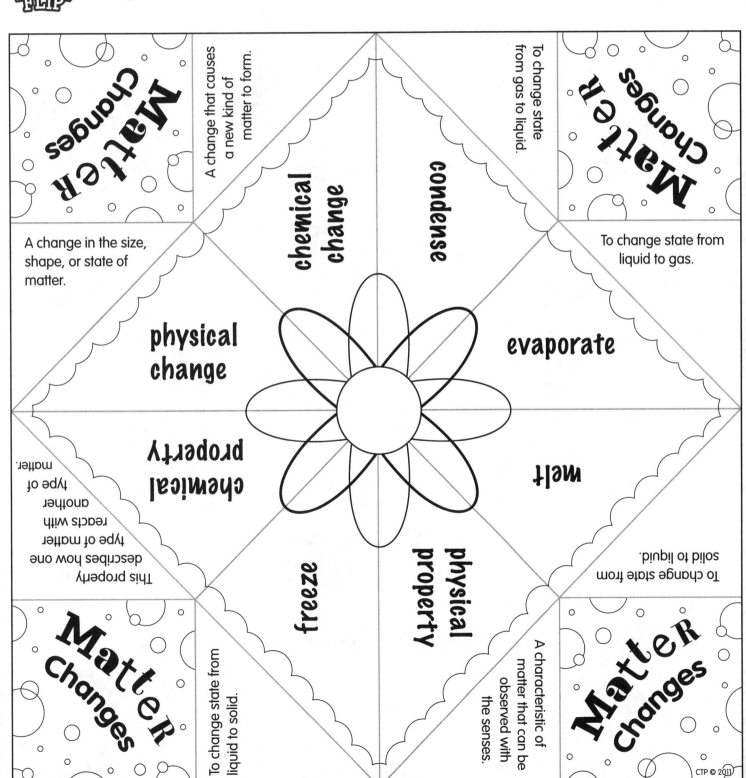

Matter Changes

A change that causes a new kind of matter to form.

To change state from gas to liquid.

Matter Changes

chemical change

condense

A change in the size, shape, or state of matter.

To change state from liquid to gas.

physical change

evaporate

chemical property

melt

This property describes how one type of matter reacts with another type of matter.

freeze

physical property

To change state from solid to liquid.

Matter Changes

To change state from liquid to solid.

A characteristic of matter that can be observed with the senses.

Matter Changes

Name _____   Date _____

Solid, Liquid, Gas

Before you "FLIP"

Hint: Matter is classified by its properties.

After you "FLIP"

On the back of this paper, name at least three examples each of a solid, liquid, and gas that can be found in your community.

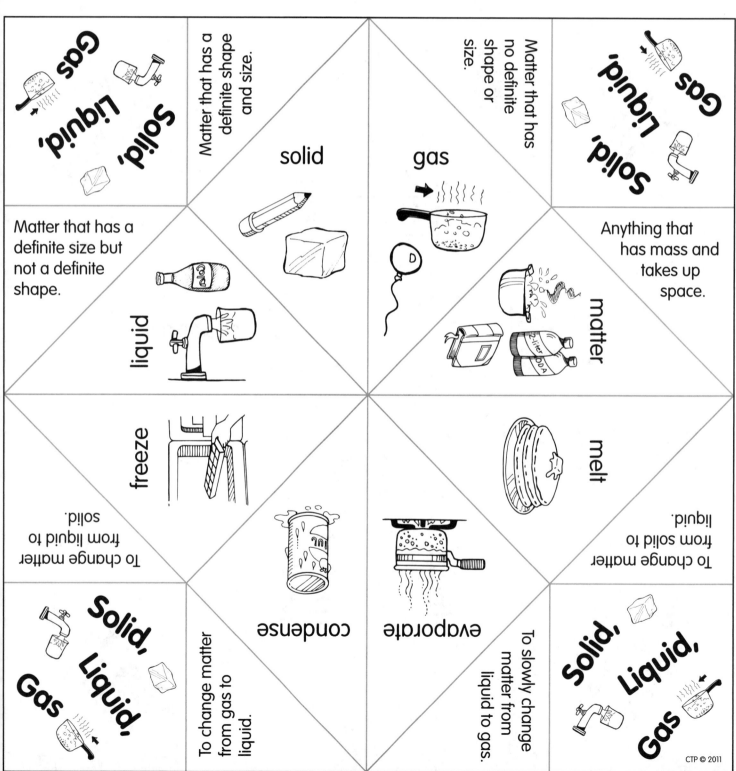

Name _____   Date _____

Energy

Hint: Energy is the ability to do work.

On the back of this paper, give two examples of kinetic energy you might see in your community.

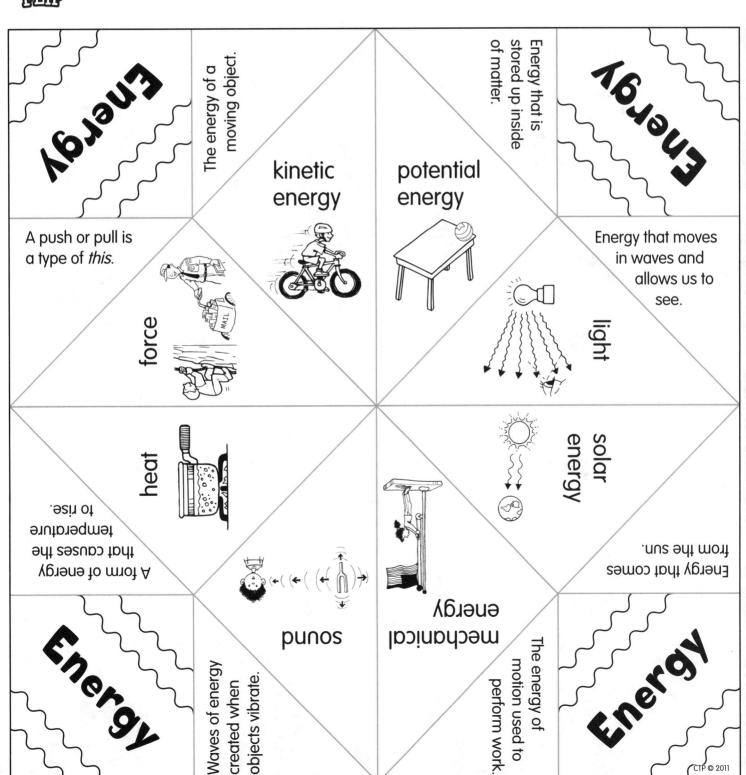

Energy

The energy of a moving object.

kinetic energy

potential energy

Energy that is stored up inside of matter.

Energy

A push or pull is a type of *this*.

force

light

Energy that moves in waves and allows us to see.

heat

solar energy

A form of energy that causes the temperature to rise.

sound

mechanical energy

Energy that comes from the sun.

Energy

Waves of energy created when objects vibrate.

The energy of motion used to perform work.

Energy

Cootie Catchers • Science • Gr. 3 © 2011 Creative Teaching Press

CTP © 2011

Name _____   Date _____

Light

Before you "FLIP"

Hint: Light travels in waves.

After you "FLIP"

On the back of this paper, list at least three examples for each kind of object: opaque, translucent, and transparent.

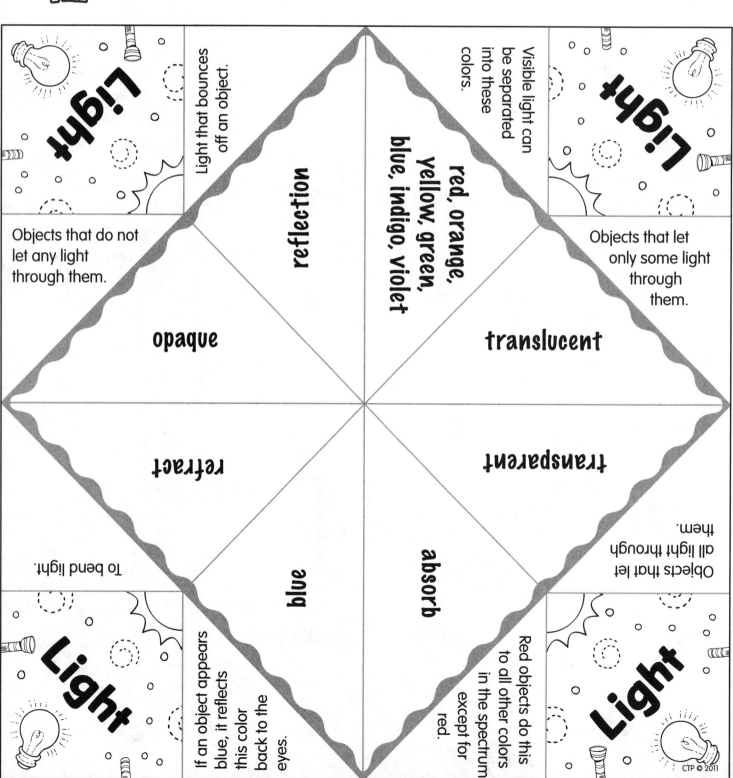

Light that bounces off an object.

Visible light can be separated into these colors.

reflection

red, orange, yellow, green, blue, indigo, violet

Objects that do not let any light through them.

opaque

translucent

Objects that let only some light through them.

refract

transparent

To bend light.

If an object appears blue, it reflects this color back to the eyes.

blue

absorb

Objects that let all light through them.

Red objects do this to all other colors in the spectrum except for red.